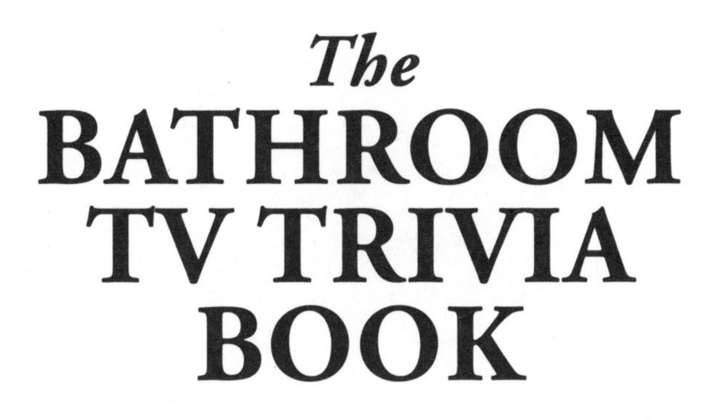

The BATHROOM TV TRIVIA BOOK

by

Jeff Kreismer

RED-LETTER PRESS, INC.
Saddle River, New Jersey

THE BATHROOM TV TRIVIA BOOK

ISBN-13: 978-1-60387-097-9
ISBN: 1-60387-097-0

Printed in the United States of America

Red-Letter Press, Inc.
P.O. Box 393
Saddle River, NJ 07458

www.Red-LetterPress.com

ACKNOWLEDGMENTS

BOOK DESIGN & TYPOGRAPHY:
Jeff Kreismer

•

COVER ART:
Jeff Godby

•

EDITORIAL:
Jack Kreismer

•

RESEARCH & DEVELOPMENT:
Rachel Jackson
Kobus Reyneke
Mike Ryan

The BATHROOM TV TRIVIA BOOK

First Things First

1. Who served as the very first host of *Saturday Night Live* in October of 1975?

a) George Carlin
b) Candice Bergen
c) Buck Henry

2. The Beatles' first American television appearance was...?

a) On the *Ed Sullivan Show*
b) On *The Huntley-Brinkley Report*, with a news piece by Edwin Newman
c) On the *CBS Evening News*, an interview with Walter Cronkite

3. The Tournament of Roses Parade on January 1, 1954, marked what first in television history?

a) The first national color broadcast
b) The first TV programming that included commercials
c) The first time an event was broadcast live

4. What married couple was the first to share a bed on television?

a) Lucy and Ricky Ricardo
b) Mary Kay and Johnny Stearns
c) Herman and Lily Munster

5. Filmed without a studio audience, what show was the first to use a laugh track on an American television series?

a) *The Hank McCune Show*
b) *I Love Lucy*
c) *The Goldbergs*

ANSWERS: 1.A (The musical guest was Janis Ian.)
2.B (1963) 3.A 4.B (1947) 5.A (1950)

Thoughts of the Throne

Every room is a bathroom when you're wearing Depends.
-Jimmy Fallon, *The Tonight Show Starring Jimmy Fallon*

The Emmys

1. What TV personality had been nominated for over 30 Emmys before finally winning for the first time in 2014 as an executive producer?

a) Bill Maher
b) Tina Fey
c) Jon Stewart

2. Months after it was canceled by ABC, what show won the Emmy for Outstanding Comedy Series in 1982?

a) *Three's Company*
b) *Barney Miller*
c) *Maude*

3. In 1999, what show became the first cable series to be nominated for an Emmy?

a) *The Sopranos*
b) *The Wire*
c) *Entourage*

MTV first aired at 12:01 AM on August 1, 1981. Appropriately, the first music video they aired was "Video Killed the Radio Star" by The Buggles.

4. In 1999, producer David E. Kelley made history by winning both the Outstanding Comedy and Outstanding Drama Emmys. What two shows were they for?

a) *The Drew Carey Show* and *L.A. Law*
b) *Spin City* and *The X-Files*
c) *Ally McBeal* and *The Practice*

5. In 2014, what show matched *Frasier's* mark when it won its fifth consecutive Emmy for Outstanding Comedy Series?

a) *The Big Bang Theory*
b) *Modern Family*
c) *Parks and Recreation*

ANSWERS: 1.A (for HBO's *Vice*) 2.B 3.A 4.C 5.B

I'm Jewish. That's no cakewalk either. Last year I was elected school treasurer. I didn't even run.

-Neal Schweiber, *Freaks and Geeks*

'50s Fodder

1. In the 1950s, there were four major networks. ABC, CBS and NBC are three. What was the fourth?

a) CRTV
b) Uniscope
c) DuMont

2. Before Dick Clark took the reigns, who was the original host of *American Bandstand* (then known as *Bandstand*) in 1952?

a) Charlie O'Donnell
b) Bob Horn
c) David Hirsch

3. Because of a contract dispute, Clayton Moore played the title character in only 75% of the episodes of what show that aired from 1949-57?

a) *Perry Mason*
b) *The Lone Ranger*
c) *Bat Masterson*

4. What '50s show that was co-created and produced by Marlo Lewis began under the name *Toast of the Town*?

a) *The Ed Sullivan Show*
b) *The Jack Benny Program*
c) *Alfred Hitchcock Presents*

5. What program, in which the family lives in two different homes during the series, was the first ever to show a toilet tank on television?

a) *Leave it to Beaver*
b) *I Love Lucy*
c) *Father Knows Best*

ANSWERS: 1.C 2.B 3.B 4.A 5.A

My wife had left me, which was very painful.
Then she came back, which was excruciating.

-Frasier Crane, *Frasier*

What's My Line?

1. What news anchor was known for his closing catchphrase "And that's the way it is"?

a) Tom Brokaw
b) Dan Rather
c) Walter Cronkite

2. The catchphrase "Dy-no-mite!" was frequently used by what sitcom character played by Jimmie Walker?

a) Dwayne Nelson from *What's Happening!!*
b) J.J. from *Good Times*
c) Tattoo from *Fantasy Island*

3. One of the most famous characters of this *Saturday Night Live* cast member was "Tommy Flanagan, the Pathological Liar", who used the old catchphrase, "Yeah! That's the ticket!" Who is he?

a) John Belushi
b) Dennis Miller
c) Jon Lovitz

4. "Do you believe in miracles?!" became one of the most famous lines ever uttered on TV after the U.S. men's hockey team upset the Soviets in the 1980 Winter Olympics. Who said it?

a) Al Michaels
b) Bob Costas
c) Dick Stockton

5. Character Frank Barone's signature line of "Holy Crap!" could be heard in what hit sitcom?

a) *All in the Family*
b) *Everybody Loves Raymond*
c) *In Living Color*

ANSWERS: 1.C 2.B 3.C 4.A 5.B (Peter Boyle was the actor.)

To paraphrase Shakespeare, it's better to have loved and lost than to stay home every night and download increasingly shameful pornography.

-Rajesh Koothrappali, *The Big Bang Theory*

Location, Location, Location

1. In 2012, NBC aired a TV special titled *Mockingbird Lane* in reference to what TV family that lived on 1313 Mockingbird Lane?

a) The Simpsons
b) The Munsters
c) The Addams Family

2. *M*A*S*H* followed a team of wartime doctors and support staff stationed in what country?

a) Korea
b) Russia
c) Japan

3. *The Oprah Winfrey Show*, which aired for 25 seasons, was based in Harpo Studios in what U.S. city?

a) Atlanta
b) Chicago
c) Dallas

Alan Thicke, who played Jason Seaver on *Growing Pains*, composed the theme songs to hit shows such as *Diff'rent Strokes*, *The Facts of Life* and *Wheel of Fortune*.

4. Just like its predecessor *Breaking Bad*, *Better Call Saul* is set and produced in what location?

a) Carson City, Nevada
b) San Jose, California
c) Albuquerque, New Mexico

5. On what fictional street did the drama from *Desperate Housewives* center?

a) Wisteria Lane
b) Centennial Street
c) Felicity Avenue

Thoughts of the Throne

On an episode of *Married...with Children*, main character Al Bundy constructed his ideal bathroom, which included five rolls of toilet paper and no sink.

The West Wing

1. What two men squared off in the first televised United States presidential debate in 1960?

a) Dwight Eisenhower and Adlai Stevenson
b) Lyndon B. Johnson and Barry Goldwater
c) John F. Kennedy and Richard Nixon

2. What *Saturday Night Live* actor, who retired as the oldest cast member in the show's history, became well-known for his impersonation of Bill Clinton?

a) Darrell Hammond
b) Phil Hartman
c) Will Forte

3. What Allstate Insurance spokesman played U.S. President David Palmer in the first five seasons of the hit Fox series *24*?

a) Charles S. Dutton
b) Dennis Haysbert
c) LeVar Burton

4. Which U.S. President appeared on the variety show *Rowan & Martin's Laugh-In* in the late 1960s?

a) Gerald Ford
b) Jimmy Carter
c) Richard Nixon

5. On what sketch comedy show, which Barack Obama himself said is "pretty good stuff," does "Luther" interpret the President's mild-mannered statements into wild outbursts as Obama's anger translator?

a) *Kroll Show*
b) *Key & Peele*
c) *Portlandia*

ANSWERS: 1.C 2.A 3.B 4.C 5.B

Manny thinks his dad is like Superman. The truth? He's a total flake. In fact, the only way he's like Superman... is that they both landed in this country illegally.

-Jay Pritchett, *Modern Family*

Behind the Music

1. Written by the show's star, what classic TV comedy began with the theme song, "You're My Greatest Love"?

a) *The Honeymooners*
b) *The Waltons*
c) *The Andy Griffith Show*

2. What three musical notes are heard in the NBC chimes that provide the audio signature for the network?

a) A, B and C
b) D, F and A
c) G, E and C

3. With a "doo-be-doo-be-doo" scat at the end of one of his songs, what singer was indirectly responsible for the naming of the *Scooby-Doo* series?

a) Dean Martin
b) Frank Sinatra
c) Sammy Davis, Jr.

4. It's well known that "Where Everybody Knows Your Name" is the theme song from *Cheers*. What's the name of the man who co-wrote and sung it?

a) Patrick Pinney
b) Vic Mizzy
c) Gary Portnoy

5. What alternative rock band wrote and recorded the theme song for *The Big Bang Theory*?

a) The Barenaked Ladies
b) Third Eye Blind
c) Red Hot Chili Peppers

ANSWERS: 1.A (It was written by Jackie Gleason.) 2.C (The General Electric Company owns NBC.) 3.B (from "Strangers in the Night") 4.C (Judy Hart Angelo was the other writer.) 5.A

If you talk to God, you're religious.
If God talks to you, you're psychotic.

-Dr. House, *House*

Two for the Money

1. Leonard Slye and Frances Octavia Smith were the real names of what famous TV married couple?

a) Roy Rogers and Dale Evans
b) Sonny & Cher
c) Captain & Tennille

2. James Arness and Milburn Stone each portrayed their characters on what TV show for 20 consecutive years?

a) *The Edge of Night*
b) *Doctor Who*
c) *Gunsmoke*

3. Before *The Tonight Show*, Johnny Carson and Ed McMahon starred together hosting what game show?

a) *The Newlywed Game*
b) *Who Do You Trust?*
c) *About Faces*

4. *Joanie Loves Chachi*, a short-lived sitcom spin-off, featured what two *Happy Days* actors?

a) Tom Bosley and Marion Ross
b) Erin Moran and Scott Baio
c) Anson Williams and Linda Goodfriend

5. In a remake of the hit show from decades earlier, what two men star as Oscar Madison and Felix Unger in the 2015 CBS version of *The Odd Couple*?

a) Matthew Perry and Thomas Lennon
b) Steve Carrell and Rainn Wilson
c) Paul Rudd and Josh Holloway

ANSWERS: 1.A 2.C 3.B 4.B 5.A

I'd rather have thieves than neighbors. The thieves don't impose. They just want your things. Neighbors want your time.

-Larry David, *Curb Your Enthusiasm*

Live Long and Prosper

1. In character, comedian and TV star Jack Benny considered himself to be what perpetual age?

a) 39
b) 45
c) 56.5

2. A panel discussion TV series hosted by Jack Barry aired from 1950-56. It was called *Life Begins at*...what age?

a) *Sixty*
b) *Seventy*
c) *Eighty*

3. At 29, what two contestants (one from Season 5, the other from Season 14) are the oldest to win the title of *American Idol*?

a) Bo Bice and Michael Johns
b) David Cook and Kris Allen
c) Taylor Hicks and Nick Fradiani

4. The youngest-ever Primetime Emmy winner was Roxana Zal, who won the 1984 award for Outstanding Supporting Actress in a Limited Series or Special for *Something About Amelia*. How old was she?

a) 6
b) 14
c) 20

5. With help from a Facebook campaign, who became the oldest person to host *Saturday Night Live* in 2010 at the age of 88?

a) Betty White
b) Clint Eastwood
c) Don Rickles

ANSWERS: 1.A 2.C 3.C 4.B 5.A

THOUGHTS OF THE THRONE

Why does toilet paper need a commercial? Who is not buying this?

-Anonymous

Seasonal Stumpers

1. Since 1952, what network has been the official broadcaster of the Macy's Thanksgiving Day Parade?

a) CBS
b) NBC
c) ABC

2. *Seinfeld* featured a holiday celebration that has since been adopted by many people who don't fit in with the other holidays. What is it?

a) Kwannukah
b) Merry Day
c) Festivus

3. Santa's Little Helper is the pet greyhound of what animated family?

a) The Simpsons
b) The Jetsons
c) The Flintstones

The first television program ever to be shown in reruns was *The Lone Ranger*.

4. In a 2000 episode of *Friends*, Ross wants to teach his son about Hanukkah. Because he's unable to find another costume, he dresses up as what?

a) Kwanzaa Kangaroo
b) Holiday Armadillo
c) Tiny Tim the Slim Jim

5. "Christmas Time is Here" is a popular song which made its first appearance in 1965 on what holiday special?

a) *Christmas Eve on Sesame Street*
b) *A Charlie Brown Christmas*
c) *Rudolph the Red-Nosed Reindeer*

ANSWERS: 1.B 2.C (It's "for the rest of us.") 3.A 4.B 5.B

Maybe that's why I like animals. Woof. Moo. Quack. They tell it like it is.

-Frank Barone, *Everybody Loves Raymond*

Strictly '60s

1. What revolutionary 1960s series included future famous names such as Robert Duvall, Dennis Hopper, Robert Redford, Burt Reynolds and Don Rickles?

a) *Star Trek: The Original Series*
b) *The Twilight Zone*
c) *Lost in Space*

2. In *The Andy Griffith Show*, the title character is a widowed sheriff of what small-town community?

a) Pine Valley, Pennsylvania
b) Capeside, Massachusetts
c) Mayberry, North Carolina

3. "The Ballad of Jed Clampett", which hit #1 on the U.S. Billboard Hot Country Singles, is the opening theme from what classic sitcom?

a) *Green Acres*
b) *The Beverly Hillbillies*
c) *Bewitched*

4. Adam West was Batman in the 1960s TV show. Who played Robin?

a) Burt Ward
b) William Dozier
c) Frank Gorshin

5. The Cartwright family was the center of this show that later aired in re-runs under the name *Ponderosa* in the early 1970s. What is it?

a) *Hogan's Heroes*
b) *Bonanza*
c) *Doctor Who*

ANSWERS: 1.B 2.C 3.B 4.A 5.B

If you can't say anything nice,
say it about Diane.

-Carla Tortelli, *Cheers*

Primetime Live

1. What 1994 sporting event was interrupted and moved to a split-screen as the infamous O.J. Simpson car chase was taking place at the same time?

a) Super Bowl
b) The Masters
c) NBA Finals

2. Who committed the first live murder on network television when he killed Lee Harvey Oswald, the assassin of President John F. Kennedy, in 1963?

a) Joseph Bonanno
b) Jack Ruby
c) Mark David Chapman

3. The tragic 1986 explosion of what NASA Space Shuttle that killed all seven aboard was seen across the United States by millions of viewers?

a) Atlantis
b) Discovery
c) Challenger

4. Before the start of Game 3 of the 1989 World Series between the A's and Giants, what natural disaster knocked the feed out of ABC's pregame coverage and ultimately postponed the Series for over a week?

a) Earthquake
b) Wildfire
c) Flood

5. On July 20, 1969, half-a-billion people worldwide watched as Apollo 11 landed on the moon. Who uttered the famous words, "That's one small step for man, one giant leap for mankind"?

a) Buzz Aldrin
b) Neil Armstrong
c) John Glenn

ANSWERS: 1.C (Knicks vs. Rockets) 2.B 3.C 4.A 5.B

My dear girl, I am a doctor. When I peek, it is in the line of duty.

-Dr. Leonard McCoy, *Star Trek*

Once Upon a Time

1. More golf is shown at this major than any other televised event, with tournament officials allowing just four minutes of commercials per hour. Which one?

a) U.S. Open
b) PGA Championship
c) The Masters

2. In what decade did *60 Minutes* make its U.S. television debut?

a) 1960s
b) 1970s
c) 1980s

3. What show's name and original format was inspired by a 1986 CBS News documentary about the drug crisis plaguing a number of U.S. neighborhoods?

a) *24*
b) *48 Hours*
c) *One Day at a Time*

4. What "timely" game show hosted by Guy Fieri aired for two seasons on NBC from 2010-11?

a) *30 Seconds to Fame*
b) *The Critical Hour*
c) *Minute to Win It*

5. Since the show's 1965 inception, the title sequence of *Days of Our Lives* has featured what time measurement object?

a) Hourglass
b) Pocket watch
c) Sundial

ANSWERS: 1.C 2.A (1968) 3.B (48 Hours on Crack Street) 4.C 5.A

Thoughts of the Throne

A new study found that nearly one out of three people can't resist using Facebook while in the bathroom. I'm just grateful they're not using Skype.
-Conan O'Brien

Cover Up

1. The inaugural cover of *TV Guide* in 1953 featured the child of the person who has appeared on *TV Guide's* cover more than anyone else. Who?

a) Elvis Presley
b) Lucille Ball
c) Johnny Carson

2. He's been a Special Agent on *NCIS* and a doctor on the 1980s Emmy-winning series *St. Elsewhere*. In 1986, he was *People* magazine's second-ever Sexiest Man Alive. He is…?

a) Michael Weatherly
b) Nick Nolte
c) Mark Harmon

3. In back-to-back years, *Entertainment Weekly* named the entire casts of two shows as "Entertainer of the Year." The years were 2005 and '06. What were the respective shows?

a) *Everybody Loves Raymond* and *The Sopranos*
b) *How I Met Your Mother* and *The Office*
c) *Lost* and *Grey's Anatomy*

4. In 1991, the year of his death, who became the first person to appear on the cover of *TV Guide* three weeks in a row?

a) Michael Landon
b) Fred Gwynne
c) Mel Blanc

5. What "First Lady of Comedy" appeared unclothed on a 2014 *Rolling Stone* cover with the U.S. Constitution written on her back that erroneously included John Hancock's signature?

a) Jennifer Aniston
b) Roseanne
c) Julia Louis-Dreyfus

ANSWERS: 1.B (son Desi Arnaz, Jr.) 2.C 3.C 4.A 5.C (Hancock signed the Declaration of Independence, not the Constitution.)

Death is just nature's way of telling you, "Hey, you're not alive anymore."

-Bull Shannon, *Night Court*

Where's the Beef?

1. What early children's TV show had the young audience seated in the "Peanut Gallery"?

a) *Winky Dink and You*
b) *Captain Kangaroo*
c) *Howdy Doody*

2. Back in the days before TV was served on satellite dishes, American TV dinners were served on foil trays. What company introduced this culinary convenience in the mid-1950s?

a) Swanson
b) Banquet
c) Stouffer's

3. What is the name of the fictional eatery that the *Seinfeld* gang frequents?

a) Tony's Place
b) Monk's Cafe
c) Dom's Diner

Wendy's founder Dave Thomas appeared in over 800 television commercials.

4. On his cooking shows, Emeril Lagasse would often utter "Kick it up a notch!" and what other exclamation?

a) "Bam!"
b) "Zoom!"
c) "Hot!"

5. Which of the following competitive cooking shows is hosted by Gordon Ramsay?

a) *Iron Chef*
b) *Top Chef*
c) *Hell's Kitchen*

ANSWERS: 1.C 2.A 3.B 4.A 5.C

Carmine and I have an understanding. I'm allowed to date other guys, and he's allowed to date ugly women.

-Shirley Feeney, *Laverne & Shirley*

Soap

1. What actress played Erica Kane in *All My Children* from the show's 1970 debut until its 2011 end on ABC?

a) Helen Wagner
b) Susan Lucci
c) Rachel Ames

2. What soap, broadcast from 1952 to 2009, is listed in "Guinness World Records" as the longest-running TV drama in history?

a) *As The World Turns*
b) *Guiding Light*
c) *One Life to Live*

3. In the 1980s, what future movie star was one of multiple actresses who played Betsy Stewart in *As The World Turns*?

a) Demi Moore
b) Julia Roberts
c) Meg Ryan

4. "Nadia's Theme", which ABC used for a montage of gymnast Nadia Comaneci's routines during the 1976 Olympics, remains the theme song of what soap?

a) *The Young and the Restless*
b) *General Hospital*
c) *Another World*

5. What *Biggest Loser* host spent over 20 years as Sami Brady on *Days of Our Lives* before deciding to join the *General Hospital* crew as a director in 2014?

a) Brooke Burns
b) Jillian Michaels
c) Alison Sweeney

ANSWERS: 1.B 2.B 3.C 4.A 5.C

You know what blows my mind? Women can see breasts any time they want. You just look down, and there they are. How you get any work done is beyond me.

-Joey Tribbiani, *Friends*

Initially Speaking

1. "D.J." is the name of a child character on two different 1990s sitcoms. What are they?

a) *Full House* and *Roseanne*
b) *Family Matters* and *Step by Step*
c) *Home Improvement* and *The Fresh Prince of Bel-Air*

2. What is Michael J. Fox's given middle name?

a) Henry
b) Andrew
c) He has no middle name.

3. While he would return a month later, Jack Paar announced his resignation from *The Tonight Show* after NBC censored a joke he told that included what initials?

a) P.M.
b) G.D.
c) W.C.

Zenith created the first TV remote control in 1950. It was called "Lazy Bones."

4. What does the "E" in "ESPN" stand for?

a) Exclusive
b) Entertainment
c) Event

5. Gordon Shumway is the real name of the lead character in what abbreviated television show?

a) *M*A*S*H*
b) *ALF*
c) *NCIS*

ANSWERS: 1.A (Tanner and Conner, respectively) 2.B 3.C (A water closet is a British term for a toilet.) 4.B (Entertainment and Sports Programming Network) 5.B (He's an Alien Life Form.)

Thoughts of the Throne

Off my case, toilet-face.
-Vinnie Barbarino's often-used phrase to the other Sweathogs whenever they bothered him, on *Welcome Back, Kotter*

That Girl

1. Through the use of revolutionary special effects, who played the dual role of herself and an identical-looking cousin named Cathy in her self-titled show?

a) Mary Tyler Moore
b) Patty Duke
c) Carol Burnett

2. What TV personality was an on-screen love interest of future real-life husband Mark Consuelos on *All My Children*?

a) Katie Couric
b) Tyra Banks
c) Kelly Ripa

3. What co-host from *The Talk* replaced Drew Carey as the new host of *Whose Line Is It Anyway?* in 2013?

a) Aisha Tyler
b) Sara Gilbert
c) Sherri Shepherd

4. What original co-host of *The View*, which debuted in 1997, was also a creator and executive producer of show?

a) Joy Behar
b) Barbara Walters
c) Meredith Vieira

5. Edith Bunker, the "dingbat" wife of Archie on *All in the Family*, was played by what stage, TV and film actress?

a) Elizabeth Montgomery
b) Jean Stapleton
c) Carroll O'Connor

ANSWERS: 1.B 2.C 3.A 4.B 5.B

Ugh, I hate January. It's dark and freezing and everyone's wearing bulky coats. You can do some serious subway flirting before you realize the guy is homeless.

-Liz Lemon, *30 Rock*

Spin City

1. After a few appearances on this show from a then-unknown Robin Williams, a.k.a. "Mork from Ork", *Mork & Mindy* was born. It is...?

a) *Three's Company*
b) *Gilligan's Island*
c) *Happy Days*

2. *Boston Legal*, which debuted in 2004, was spawned from what ABC show that won the Emmy in 1998 and '99 for Best Drama Series?

a) *ER*
b) *The Practice*
c) *Law & Order*

3. While it later aired in syndication as part of the *Saved by the Bell* series, this show actually preceded the hit sitcom. What was it called?

a) *I Heard a Screech*
b) *By the Belding*
c) *Good Morning, Miss Bliss*

4. While *The Cosby Show* was still airing in the late-1980s, Lisa Bonet reprised her role as Densise Huxtable on a new sitcom. What was it?

a) *Head of the Class*
b) *A Different World*
c) *Too Close for Comfort*

5. After appearing on the first two seasons of *Diff'rent Strokes*, housekeeper Mrs. Garrett (Charlotte Rae) became the focus of a new show that wound up lasting nine seasons. What was it?

a) *The Facts of Life*
b) *The Golden Girls*
c) *Family Ties*

ANSWERS: 1.C 2.B 3.C 4.B 5.A

Everyone thinks I'm a hypochondriac.
It makes me sick.

-Felix Unger, *The Odd Couple*

The Long and Short of It

1. Beginning in 1947, what is the longest-running TV show in American broadcasting history?

a) *The Tonight Show*
b) *Meet the Press*
c) *Face the Nation*

2. Launched in the United States in 2010, ShortsHD is a channel that airs what?

a) Short-lived TV series that previously aired on major networks
b) Short films, including those nominated for Academy Awards
c) Shortened versions of major sporting events

3. Who holds the Guinness World Record for the most time spent in front of a television camera?

a) Regis Philbin
b) Barbara Walters
c) Hugh Downs

Jerry Seinfeld reportedly declined an offer of $5 million per episode to continue *Seinfeld*.

4. What are the names of the two characters created by Martin Short that went on to star in their own shows?

a) Jimmy Short and Timmy Shorter
b) Carlos Hafner and Raymond Wilfer
c) Jiminy Glick and Ed Grimley

5. What is the name of the TLC reality show starring Theresa Caputo that began airing in 2011?

a) *Life's Too Short*
b) *The Long Island Medium*
c) *The Shortest Woman Alive*

ANSWERS: 1.B 2.B 3.A 4.C 5.B

If I had a nickel for every time a girl dumped me, disappeared for five years, and came back as a guy...I'd have a nickel.

-Charlie Harper, *Two and a Half Men*

Be My Guest

1. The NBA's all-time leading scorer appeared as himself on an episode of *Full House* in which Uncle Jesse is trying to learn how to shoot for a celebrity game. Who is he?

a) Wilt Chamberlain
b) Oscar Robertson
c) Kareem Abdul-Jabbar

2. In a famous episode of *All in the Family*, what singing star appears at the Bunkers' home to pick up a briefcase he left in Archie's taxicab?

a) Sammy Davis, Jr.
b) Elvis Presley
c) James Brown

3. On *The Brady Bunch*, Marcia prematurely promises her school that she can get a pop star to perform at her prom. Who saves the day by appearing at her front door and asking her to be his date?

a) Davy Jones
b) Rod Stewart
c) Jermaine Jackson

4. What First Lady appeared in a special episode of *Diff'rent Strokes* to promote her "Just Say No" campaign?

a) Barbara Bush
b) Eleanor Rosalynn Carter
c) Nancy Reagan

5. Along with a $60,000 prototype doll of the star, what singer played herself on a 2000 episode of *Will and Grace*?

a) Mariah Carey
b) Madonna
c) Cher

ANSWERS: 1.C 2.A 3.A 4.C 5.C

Thoughts of the Throne

Maybe they should have a toilet paper museum. Would you like that? So we can see all the toilet paper advancements down through the ages. Toilet paper in the Crusades: The development of the perforation. The first six-pack. **-Jerry Seinfeld**

That ’70s Show

1. What original 1975 *Saturday Night Live* cast member spent only two seasons on the show?

a) Chevy Chase
b) Gilda Radner
c) Bill Murray

2. What groundbreaking TV program featured a never-married, independent career woman as its central character?

a) *Three's Company*
b) *All in the Family*
c) *The Mary Tyler Moore Show*

3. Every episode of *The Muppet Show* featured a human guest star. What was unique about the premise?

a) Each guest was required to both sing and act during their appearance.
b) No guest ever appeared more than once.
c) All guests had to be screened by an animal rights group before being allowed on the show.

4. The term "jumping the shark", used to describe something that has begun to decline in quality, originated from a 1977 episode in which a character from what show literally jumped over a shark on water skis?

a) *Monty Python's Flying Circus*
b) *The Brady Bunch*
c) *Happy Days*

5. What does *M*A*S*H** stand for?

a) Military Arms Soldier Housing
b) Mobile Army Surgical Hospital
c) Modern Armies Serving Heaven

ANSWERS: 1.A 2.C 3.B 4.C (Fonzie was the character.) 5.B

Whenever I get depressed, I raise my hemlines.
If things don't change, I am bound to be arrested.

-Ally McBeal

The Midnight Special

1. What late-night TV host previously worked as a writer and producer for *The Simpsons*?

a) Conan O'Brien
b) Craig Ferguson
c) Seth Meyers

2. Who hosted *The Tonight Show* from 1957-62 before Johnny Carson took over for him?

a) Steve Allen
b) Jack Paar
c) Jack Lescoulie

3. Which program taped in the theater that was home to *The Ed Sullivan Show* for over 20 years?

a) *The Late Show with David Letterman* (now *Stephen Colbert*)
b) *The Tonight Show with Jay Leno*
c) *Late Night with Conan O'Brien*

In *Game of Thrones*, Harry Lloyd, who plays Viserys Targaryen, is a great-great-great grandson of Charles Dickens. Oona Chaplin (Talisa Maegyr) is the granddaughter of Charlie Chaplin.

4. What group has been Jimmy Fallon's house band since 2009, when he first started on late night TV?

a) The Max Weinberg 7
b) The Roots
c) The Clash

5. On *Jimmy Kimmel Live!*, Kimmel frequently ends his show with, "Our apologies to ______ ________, we ran out of time." What celebrity fills in the blanks?

a) Matt Damon
b) Sandra Bullock
c) Brad Pitt

ANSWERS: 1.A 2.B 3.A (in New York) 4.B 5.A

I'm not proud of being an alcoholic drug addict. I'm not proud of biting the head off a bat... But I'm a real guy. To be Ozzy Osbourne, it could be worse. I could be Sting.

-Ozzy Osbourne, *The Osbournes*

My Secret Identity

1. Joyce Penelope Wilhelmina Frankenberg was *Dr. Quinn, Medicine Woman*. By what name is she better known?

a) Julie Andrews
b) Jacqueline Bisset
c) Jane Seymour

2. Caryn Johnson was a co-producer of *Hollywood Squares* before joining *The View* a few years later. Who is she?

a) Sherri Shepherd
b) Whoopi Goldberg
c) Star Jones

3. Miley Cyrus played teen idol Miley Stewart on the Disney Channel's *Hannah Montana*. Her birth name, however, isn't Miley. What is it?

a) Angel
b) Bambi
c) Destiny

4. Before she became a household name under a different name, Stefani Germanotta appeared on an episode of MTV's *Boiling Points* in 2005. Who is she?

a) Adele
b) Lady Gaga
c) Katy Perry

5. What is the real last name of father and son acting tandem Martin and Charlie Sheen?

a) Estevez
b) Henriquez
c) Vasquez

ANSWERS: 1.C 2.B 3.C 4.B 5.A

To me, religion is like Paul Rudd. I see the appeal, and I would never take it away from anyone, but I would also never stand in line for it.

-Jeff Winger, *Community*

Color My World

1. What was the name of Betty White's character on *The Golden Girls*?

a) Rose Nylund
b) Violet Plimpton
c) Amber Foster

2. During the 1992 presidential campaign, Dan Quayle scolded what show for having its main character decide to bear a child outside of marriage?

a) *Orphan Black*
b) *Murphy Brown*
c) *In Living Color*

3. "Reagan's Theme", playing off the last name of the lead characters, is the music that is heard in the opening of what police drama?

a) *Blue Heelers*
b) *Blue Bloods*
c) *NYPD Blue*

4. What former *Star Trek* actress stars as Galina "Red" Reznikov in the Netflix series *Orange Is the New Black*?

a) Kate Mulgrew
b) Jennifer Lien
c) Taryn Manning

5. Nearly three decades after appearing in the movie *Pretty In Pink*, what actor took on the role of Raymond "Red" Reddington in the NBC crime drama *The Blacklist*?

a) Andrew McCarthy
b) Paul Reubens
c) James Spader

ANSWERS: 1.A 2.B 3.B 4.A 5.C

Thoughts of the Throne

When Johnny Carson hosted *The Tonight Show*, he once joked about a scarcity of toilet paper during his monologue. It created a nationwide run on the product, causing a real shortage.

Networking

1. Which station has been referred to as the "Eye Network" and the "Tiffany Network"?

a) ABC
b) CBS
c) UPN

2. The headquarters for what cable network, launched in 1979, are in Bristol, Connecticut?

a) CNN
b) MTV
c) ESPN

3. Which two major networks still operate under a 720p high definition signal rather than the higher 1080i picture quality?

a) ABC and FOX
b) NBC and CBS
c) FOX and NBC

Baseball's World Series was televised for the first time in 1947. The New York Yankees defeated the Brooklyn Dodgers, featuring rookie Jackie Robinson, four games to three.

4. What premium network has operated under the slogans "Just You Wait", "Something Special's On" and "So Original"?

a) Starz
b) Showtime
c) HBO

5. What New York-based cable station owned by NBCUniversal launched in 1977 as Madison Square Garden Network before switching to its current name just three years later?

a) Lifetime
b) USA
c) AMC

ANSWERS: 1.B 2.C 3.A 4.C 5.B

Beauty is in the eye of the beholder, and it may be necessary from time to time to give a stupid or misinformed beholder a black eye.

-Miss Piggy, *The Muppet Show*

Brought To You By...

1. Justin Long, known more recently on TV for his Apple commercials and "Get a Mac" advertising campaign, played Warren Cheswick on what early 2000s show?

a) *Gilmore Girls*
b) *Malcolm in the Middle*
c) *Ed*

2. After a child offers him a Coca-Cola following a rough game, what "Mean" Steelers player chugs the drink before tossing the kid his jersey in the famous, "Hey Kid, Catch" TV spot?

a) Bubba Bean
b) Fred Dean
c) Joe Greene

3. "You Got the Right One, Baby" was a popular Diet Pepsi jingle that featured what musician in its commercials?

a) Stevie Wonder
b) Ray Charles
c) Billy Joel

4. After a 20-year run, the famous "Got Milk?" ads featuring celebrity milk mustaches were retired in 2014 and replaced by what new tagline?

a) Milk Life
b) Milky Smooth
c) Milking It

5. Terry Tate, Office Linebacker, "gives out the pain" by tackling uncooperative employees in a 2003 Super Bowl commercial promoting what brand?

a) Nike
b) Reebok
c) Adidas

ANSWERS: 1.C 2.C 3.B 4.A 5.B

Gee, your kitchen always looks so clean. My mother says it looks as though you never do any work in here.

-Eddie Haskell, *Leave It to Beaver,* to June Cleaver

Humble Beginnings

1. The first three episodes of this show, with a working title of *Oil*, were broadcast as a three-hour event in 1981. What is it?

a) *Dynasty*
b) *Hill Street Blues*
c) *Knight Rider*

2. In its original pilot, Jerry and George appeared, but there was no Elaine. Kramer was referred to as Kessler. The show was first called *The Seinfeld*....what?

a) *Crew*
b) *Conundrum*
c) *Chronicles*

3. In an unaired pilot episode of *True Blood*, Brook Kerr portrayed what character before being replaced by Rutina Wesley for the role?

a) Sookie Stackhouse
b) Tara Thornton
c) Arlene Fowler

4. Christina Applegate uttered the first-ever words of this sitcom when her character exclaimed, “Let go of my hair you little psychopath!” What’s the show?

a) *Married…with Children*
b) *Modern Family*
c) *Malcolm in the Middle*

5. At over $10 million, co-creator and director J.J. Abrams held nothing back for what became the most expensive pilot in TV history when it aired. What show was it?

a) *Boardwalk Empire*
b) *Lost*
c) *Game of Thrones*

ANSWERS: 1.A 2.C 3.B 4.A 5.B

Here’s a job I could do: “Police seek third gunman.” Well, tomorrow I’m gonna march over to the police station and tell them that I’m the man they’re looking for!

-Harry Solomon, *3rd Rock from the Sun*

Get Real

1. Credited with launching the modern reality TV boom, what show was inspired by a 1973 PBS documentary series, *An American Family*?

a) *Bug Juice*
b) *True Life*
c) *The Real World*

2. Javier Colon was the winner of the inaugural season of what reality TV show?

a) *American Idol*
b) *The Voice*
c) *The X-Factor*

3. In the early 2000s, TV personality Elisabeth Hasselbeck (then Elisabeth Filarski) was a contestant on the second season of what reality show?

a) *Survivor*
b) *Big Brother*
c) *The Bachelor*

4. TLC's *Here Comes Honey Boo Boo* focused on the family of a child beauty pageant contestant, "Honey Boo Boo." What's her real name?

a) Trista Rehn
b) Alana Thompson
c) Jessica Shannon

5. Teamed with Cheryl Burke, in 2006, what football star became the first athlete to be crowned a champion on *Dancing with the Stars*?

a) Emmitt Smith
b) Lawrence Taylor
c) Hines Ward

ANSWERS: 1.C 2.B 3.A 4.B 5.A

Thoughts of the Throne

3% of Americans have televisions in their bathroom.

Boob Tube to Big Screen

1. Long before the 1993 movie, main character Dr. Richard Kimble is falsely convicted of his wife's murder in what hit 1960s TV series?

a) *The Firm*
b) *The Unusual Suspects*
c) *The Fugitive*

2. *Da Ali G Show* was an HBO fixture in the early 2000s before it spawned three movies (*Ali G*, *Borat* and *Bruno*) featuring characters all played by what man?

a) Sacha Baron Cohen
b) Ken Davitian
c) Clifford Banagale

3. Before the movie franchise that began in the 1990s with protagonist Ethan Hunt, Dan Briggs and Jim Phelps were lead characters in what TV series that aired from 1966-73?

a) *Die Hard*
b) *Mission: Impossible*
c) *Jurassic Park*

4. What 1980 movie was the first feature length film to have been based off of a *Saturday Night Live* skit?

a) *Stripes*
b) *The Spy Who Loved Me*
c) *The Blues Brothers*

5. As actors from the original TV series, Barbara Billingsley, Ken Osmond and Frank Bank all had cameos in what 1997 movie that was widely panned by critics?

a) *Leave It to Beaver*
b) *The Honeymooners*
c) *The Brady Bunch*

ANSWERS: 1.C 2.A 3.B 4.C 5.A

Look, this is an odd question, but you're kind of cute and you're pretty nice to me. Are you drunk? It's OK if you are.

-Drew Carey, *The Drew Carey Show*

By The Numbers

1. On *Gilligan's Island*, how many people were shipwrecked?

a) 5
b) 7
c) 9

2. Including parents, kids, and housekeeper Alice, how many members of *The Brady Bunch* were there?

a) 9
b) 10
c) 11

3. The mystical numbers 4, 8, 15, 16, 23, and 42 appear throughout what 2000s TV series?

a) *Prison Break*
b) *Lost*
c) *Dexter*

Family Guy **creator Seth MacFarlane was scheduled to be on American Airlines Flight 11 from Boston to L.A., which crashed into the World Trade Center on the morning of September 11, 2001. He was late to the airport and missed his flight.**

4. Because his phone number was similar to 555-FILM, what *Seinfeld* character continued to get calls for Moviefone before deciding to play along and give out movie times to callers?

a) Jerry
b) Kramer
c) George

5. Former CBS show *Numbers* was stylized with what actual number present in the show's title?

a) 3
b) 5
c) 8

ANSWERS: 1.B ("...Gilligan, the Skipper too, the Millionaire, and his Wife, the Movie Star, the Professor and Mary Ann, here on Gilligan's Isle.") 2.A 3.B 4.B 5.A (*NUMB3RS*)

Divorce is very difficult, especially on the kids. Of course, I'm the result of my parents having stayed together, so you never know.

-George Costanza, *Seinfeld*

Oh Captain, My Captain

1. In *Star Trek: The Original Series*, one of the first interracial kisses shown on TV took place when Captain James T. Kirk (William Shatner) planted one on what character portrayed by Nichelle Nichols?

a) Christine Chapel
b) Janice Rand
c) Nyota Uhura

2. *Captain Caveman and the Teen Angels* was an animated series that aired in the late-1970s as a takeoff from what cartoon series?

a) *Schoolhouse Rock!*
b) *Scooby-Doo, Where Are You!*
c) *Popeye the Sailor*

3. Malcolm Reynolds, also known as Captain Tight Pants, was the lead character on what short-lived 2002 TV show that ultimately spawned a film and other media opportunities?

a) *Firefly*
b) *Twilight*
c) *Moonlight*

4. Because the character's real name, S.S. Minnow Captain Jonas Grumby, was rarely used after the show's pilot, he's known more familiarly in TV lore as whom?

a) Hawkeye from *M*A*S*H*
b) Captain Stubing from *The Love Boat*
c) The Skipper from *Gilligan's Island*

5. Which of these *Star Trek* captains was the first female commanding officer to play a lead role in the series?

a) Picard
b) Sisko
c) Janeway

ANSWERS: 1.C 2.B 3.A 4.C 5.C (Captain Kathryn Janeway, played by Kate Mulgrew)

Abraham Lincoln once said that, "If you're a racist, I will attack you with the North," and these are the principles I carry with me in the workplace.

-Michael Scott, *The Office*

The Voice

1. What 1990s sitcom star provided the voice of the future Ted Mosby on *How I Met Your Mother*?

a) Tim Allen
b) Michael Richards
c) Bob Saget

2. In 2010, what movie star replaced the late Walter Cronkite as the voice of the introduction to the *CBS Evening News*?

a) Robert Redford
b) Morgan Freeman
c) Jack Nicholson

3. While also known for his movie work, he was the narrator on *The Wonder Years* as the adult Kevin Arnold. Later, he was *Dilbert* on the animated TV series. Who is he?

a) Daniel Stern
b) Chris Elliott
c) Dan Lauria

4. What country tunesmith performed the theme song and narrated the episodes of *The Dukes of Hazzard*?

a) Gary Morris
b) Waylon Jennings
c) Dwight Yoakam

5. "Charlie" in *Charlie's Angels* was only heard over the phone as he contacted his female sleuths. Who is he?

a) John Forsythe
b) David Doyle
c) Ben Roberts

ANSWERS: 1.C 2.B 3.A 4.B 5.A

Thoughts of the Throne

Howie Mandel was once the butt of a practical joke when his California house was TP'd with more than 4,000 rolls of toilet paper. The perpetrators were TV prankster Roman Atwood and Mandel's own son.

Entirely '80s

1. What show, which debuted in 1987, was the first prime-time television series to air on Fox?

a) *The A-Team*
b) *Dukes of Hazzard*
c) *Married...with Children*

2. This show, with an original working title of *Gold Coast*, was "the first show to look really new and different since color TV was invented" according to *People* magazine. What is it?

a) *Magnum, P.I.*
b) *The Transformers*
c) *Miami Vice*

3. On *Cheers*, what was the former occupation of bartender Sam "Mayday" Malone, played by Ted Danson?

a) Boston Red Sox relief pitcher
b) Aerosmith cover band guitarist
c) Fruit of the Loom underwear model

4. President Ronald Reagan once stated that this show, which featured a Young Republican as its main character, was a favorite of his. It is…?

a) *Knight Rider*
b) *Family Ties*
c) *The Wonder Years*

5. On *The Cosby Show*, what is the name of the fictional historically black college that both Cliff and Clair Huxtable attended?

a) Hudson University
b) Hamilton State
c) Hillman College

ANSWERS: 1.C 2.C 3.A 4.B (Alex P. Keaton, played by Michael J. Fox) 5.C

Due to the shape of the North American elk's esophagus, even if it could speak, it could not pronounce the word "lasagna."

-Cliff Clavin, *Cheers*

Doctor Who

1. Hugh Laurie played a free-wheeling, brilliant diagnostician on *House*. What is Dr. House's first name?

a) Gregory
b) Samuel
c) Matthew

2. The first name of Dr. Oz and the last name of Dr. Phil begin with the same letter. What is it?

a) B
b) H
c) M

3. Before he became a household name, who starred as Dr. Philip Chandler in NBC's hospital drama *St. Elsewhere* during the 1980s?

a) Denzel Washington
b) Tom Cruise
c) George Clooney

In the fourth season of *The Simpsons*, Elizabeth Taylor appeared for the voicing of Maggie's first word.

4. What medical drama that aired from 1969-76 starred Robert Young and a young James Brolin?

a) *Dr. Kildare*
b) *Dr. Finlay's Casebook*
c) *Marcus Welby, M.D.*

5. Dr. John Carter was introduced in the pilot episode of *ER* and appeared for 11 consecutive seasons. Who portrayed him?

a) Paul McCrane
b) Noah Wyle
c) Alex Kingston

ANSWERS: 1.A 2.C (Mehmet and McGraw, respectively) 3.A 4.C 5.B

We're sorry to bother you at such a time like this, Mrs. Twice. We would have come earlier, but your husband wasn't dead then.

-Det. Frank Drebin, *Police Squad!*

The Super Bowl

1. What two networks televised the very first Super Bowl (Packers vs. Chiefs) in the late 1960s?

a) CBS and NBC
b) NBC and ABC
c) CBS and ABC

2. With help from Justin Timberlake, whose "wardrobe malfunction" was seen by over 140 million during the halftime show at Super Bowl XXXVIII?

a) Britney Spears
b) Madonna
c) Janet Jackson

3. To increase viewership, the 1993 Super Bowl halftime show featured one star performer for the first time. Who was it?

a) Whitney Houston
b) Billy Joel
c) Michael Jackson

4. After Super Bowl XXI, who became the first Super Bowl MVP to utter the now-famous phrase "I'm going to Disney World" on TV?

a) Phil Simms
b) John Elway
c) Joe Montana

5. "The One After the Super Bowl" aired in 1996 and became the highest-rated Super Bowl lead out program ever. What was the show?

a) *Friends*
b) *Seinfeld*
c) *Everybody Loves Raymond*

ANSWERS: 1.A 2.C 3.C 4.A 5.A

I just thank God
I'm an atheist.

-Mike Stivic, *All in the Family*

Bowling for Dollars

1. In 1999, who became the first person to win the million bucks on *Who Wants to Be a Millionaire*?

a) John Carpenter
b) Tom Christopher
c) Joe Carter

2. Since 2005, this animated personality and former hedge fund manager has hosted *Mad Money*, the finance-based CNBC program. Who is he?

a) Bill Griffeth
b) Tyler Mathisen
c) Jim Cramer

3. In 1984, Michael Larson won over $100,000 on what game show after memorizing the supposedly random patterns of the game board to stop it where he wanted?

a) *Jackpot*
b) *Gambit*
c) *Press Your Luck*

4. On what Bravo reality show did Patti Stanger set up wealthy singles as the CEO of the Beverly Hills Millionaires Club?

a) *One in a Million*
b) *Millionaire Matchmaker*
c) *Dollars and Sense*

5. On this Comedy Central show that began airing in the late 1990s, contestants competed to "*Win _____ ______'s Money.*" Whose money was it?

a) *Ben Stein's*
b) *Donald Trump's*
c) *James Carville's*

ANSWERS: 1.A 2.C 3.C 4.B 5.A

THOUGHTS OF THE THRONE

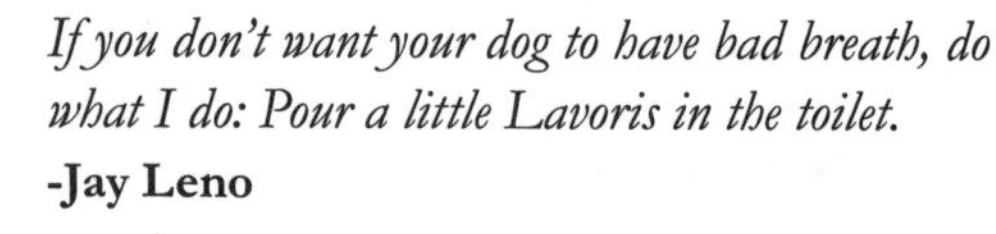

If you don't want your dog to have bad breath, do what I do: Pour a little Lavoris in the toilet.
-Jay Leno

Name's The Same

1. The real name of the character portrayed by Rob McElhenney on *It's Always Sunny in Philadelphia* is that of a memorable figure who first appeared on TV in the early 1960s. What is it?

a) Soupy Sales
b) Ronald McDonald
c) Marcel Marceau

2. What 2013 *Saturday Night Live* host shares their name with a famous character from *The Honeymooners*?

a) Andrew Garfield
b) Kerry Washington
c) Edward Norton

3. Which of the following was the full name of a character on both *ER* and *Friends*?

a) Rachel Greene
b) Jackie Robbins
c) Monica Price

4. Before "Uncle Jesse" (John Stamos) became famous on *Full House*, it was the name of a character played by Denver Pyle on what show a decade earlier?

a) *One Day at a Time*
b) *The Waltons*
c) *The Dukes of Hazzard*

5. Dr. Mark Sloan is portrayed by two actors, Dick Van Dyke and Eric Dane, in two different shows. What are they?

a) *Northern Exposure* and *Lost*
b) *Diagnosis Murder* and *Grey's Anatomy*
c) *Chicago Hope* and *Nip/Tuck*

ANSWERS: 1.B (Mac is the character.) 2.C 3.A 4.C 5.B

I don't know how we're going to explain to our friends that we spent several years with people who aren't even in the social register.

-Lovey Howell, *Gilligan's Island*

Now Streaming

1. Netflix was founded in 1997 in Scotts Valley, California by what two men?

a) Shawn Jasper and Kevin Kane
b) Jim Hanks and Jeff Bezos
c) Marc Randolph and Reed Hastings

2. Which Netflix program was a continuation of a previously canceled TV series and not an original production?

a) *Arrested Development*
b) *Orange is the New Black*
c) *Bad Samaritans*

3. What Emmy Award-nominated Netflix thriller series is set in a fictional Pennsylvania town and based on a novel of the same name written by Brian McGreevy?

a) *Marco Polo*
b) *Hemlock Grove*
c) *Lilyhammer*

4. What actor stars as politician Frank Underwood in the Netflix hit series *House of Cards*?

a) David Spade
b) Kevin Spacey
c) Kevin Bacon

5. Charlie Cox stars as *Daredevil* in the critically acclaimed Netflix series that premiered in 2015. What is the name of the alter ego of the Marvel character?

a) Matt Murdock
b) Charlie Connors
c) Phil Porter

ANSWERS: 1.C 2.A 3.B 4.B 5.A

This looks like a job for the Masked Avenger...
but since he's not around, I guess I'll have to do it.

-Bugs Bunny

Real Sports

1. What ABC television show that ran for 37 years opened with "the thrill of victory and the agony of defeat"?

a) *Monday Night Football*
b) *American Gladiators*
c) *Wide World of Sports*

2. NFL kicker Rolf Benirschke briefly hosted the daytime version of what game show in 1989?

a) *Wheel of Fortune*
b) *Jeopardy!*
c) *Family Feud*

3. What old-time Yankees play-by-play man was the first host of *This Week in Baseball*?

a) Vin Scully
b) Mel Allen
c) Howard Cosell

***Mad Men* was the first basic cable series to win an Emmy for Outstanding Drama Series, doing so in each of its first four seasons.**

4. In 2013, what singer took over for Faith Hill on NBC's *Sunday Night Football* opening?

a) Carrie Underwood
b) Miranda Lambert
c) Kelly Clarkson

5. This *SportsCenter* anchor returned to ESPN in 2013 to host his own show after a decade on his political news program, *Countdown*. He is...?

a) Craig Kilborn
b) Keith Olbermann
c) Dan Patrick

ANSWERS: 1.C 2.A 3.B 4.A 5.B

I like school...It's a good way to kill time between weekends.

-Zack Morris, *Saved by the Bell*

Foreign Flavor

1. Before there was *Dancing with the Stars* in America, there was *Strictly Come Dancing* in the UK. What two judges from the British show have been on the U.S. version since its inception?

a) David Arch and Alan Dedicoat
b) Bruno Tonioli and Len Goodman
c) Arlene Phillips and Craig Revel Horwood

2. What American TV series is based on the Israeli version called *Hatufim*, which translates to "Prisoners of War"?

a) The Walking Dead
b) Game of Thrones
c) Homeland

3. The Dutch game show *Miljoenenjacht* debuted in 2000. The American version originally aired from 2005-09. What is it?

a) *Are You Smarter Than a 5th Grader?*
b) *Deal or No Deal*
c) *Weakest Link*

4. This American reality TV program was originally created by Brit Charlie Parsons before it aired in Sweden in 1997 under the name *Expedition: Robinson*. What is it?

a) *The Simple Life*
b) *The Amazing Race*
c) *Survivor*

5. Fittingly, it was America Ferrera who starred in what 2000s U.S. show that was based off of a Columbian soap opera?

a) *Ugly Betty*
b) *Gilmore Girls*
c) *The O.C.*

ANSWERS: 1.B 2.C 3.B 4.C 5.A (*Yo soy Betty, la fea* is the show.)

Thoughts of the Throne

The average human will spend three years on the throne, nothing compared to the nine years spent watching TV in a lifetime.

The Gig That Got Away

1. What late-night personality never returned Jerry Seinfeld's call when he was offered the role of George Costanza before Jason Alexander became synonymous with the character?

a) Steve Higgins
b) Andy Richter
c) Paul Shaffer

2. While Ryan Seacrest has been with *American Idol* since its inception, he had a co-host who left the show after its first season back in 2002. Who was it?

a) Kirk Fox
b) Ben Gleib
c) Brian Dunkleman

3. Dana Delany turned down the role of Carrie Bradshaw on *Sex and the City*. It was ultimately given to an actress who won multiple Golden Globes and Emmys playing the part. Who?

a) Sarah Jessica Parker
b) Eva Longoria
c) Kristin Davis

4. Fresh off his hit movie *Sideways*, what actor declined the part of Michael Scott in *The Office* before it was given to Steve Carell?

a) Thomas Haden Church
b) Paul Giamatti
c) Jon Hamm

5. While both men have already had successful careers, they both reportedly passed on what would become a legendary role for Bryan Cranston – *Breaking Bad's* Walter White. Who are they?

a) Nicolas Cage and Billy Bob Thornton
b) Matthew Broderick and John Cusack
c) Steve Buscemi and Ralph Fiennes

ANSWERS: 1.C 2.C 3.A 4.B 5.B

In a courtroom, reasonable doubt can get you off for murder. In an engagement, it makes you feel like a bad person.

-Miranda Hobbes, *Sex and the City*

Second Guessing

1. Who was the second actor to play television detective *Columbo*?

a) Peter Falk
b) Jack Webb
c) Efrem Zimbalist Jr.

2. Art Fleming was the first host of the long-running *Jeopardy!* game show. Who was the second?

a) Johnny Gilbert
b) Alex Trebek
c) Don Pardo

3. Who hosted the Primetime Emmy Awards for the first time in 2009 and then a second in 2013?

a) Conan O'Brien
b) Ryan Seacrest
c) Neil Patrick Harris

***Wheel of Fortune's* letter turner Vanna White claps her hands an average of 720 times per episode.**

4. Two actors portrayed Darrin Stephens on *Bewitched*. The first was Dick York. Who was the second?

a) Dick Sargent
b) George Tobias
c) Paul Lynde

5. What Canadian sketch comedy show starring the likes of John Candy and Catherine O'Hara began airing in the United States during its second season in the mid-1970s?

a) *Second Time Around*
b) *Second Thoughts*
c) *Second City Television*

ANSWERS: 1.A (Bert Freed was the first.) 2.B (since 1984) 3.C 4.A 5.C

Fate is what you call it when you don't know the name of the person screwing you over.

-Lois, *Malcolm in the Middle*

'90s Nostalgia

1. From 1994-99, two men each won three Emmys for Outstanding Lead Actor in a Comedy Series. Who were they?

a) Garry Shandling and John Goodman
b) Kelsey Grammer and John Lithgow
c) Jerry Seinfeld and Paul Reiser

2. While he made his TV acting debut nearly two decades earlier, on what show did George Clooney gain wide recognition as Douglas Ross?

a) *Law and Order*
b) *ER*
c) *X-Files*

3. In *Seinfeld* lore, what character, whose name is revealed as Yev Kassem in the finale, was played by Larry Thomas?

a) The Soup Nazi
b) Newman
c) Bob Sacamano

4. What variety show was responsible for producing a series of shorts featuring *The Simpsons* before the animated family earned its own hit show?

a) *The Lawrence Welk Show*
b) *The Arsenio Hall Show*
c) *The Tracey Ullman Show*

5. Before his days on *Friends*, what actor had minor roles on *The Wonder Years*, *Blossom* and *NYPD Blue*?

a) Matthew Perry
b) David Schwimmer
c) Matt LeBlanc

ANSWERS: 1.B (for *Frasier* and *3rd Rock from the Sun*, respectively) 2.B 3.A 4.C 5.B

You'd better watch who you're calling a child, Lois. Because if I'm a child, you know what that makes you? A pedophile. And I'll be damned if I'm gonna be lectured by a pervert.

-Peter Griffin, *Family Guy*

Pet-Pourri

1. What is the name of the anthropomorphic dog on *Family Guy*?

a) Brian Griffin
b) Peter Griffin
c) Stewie Griffin

2. For what animal-related activity is Allan Lane best known?

a) He voiced all the dolphin sound effects in the 1960s TV series *Flipper*.
b) He was the voice of the talking horse, Mister Ed.
c) He trained all 11 dogs that played "Lassie" in the movie and TV series.

3. Eddie, a Jack Russell Terrier, often stole the show as one of the featured characters in what sitcom?

a) *Mad About You*
b) *Frasier*
c) *Coach*

4. During the beginning of *Friends*, Ross introduced Marcel, an illegal exotic animal that went on to a film career after Ross had to give him up. What was Marcel?

a) Flying squirrel
b) Capuchin monkey
c) Wallaby

5. Who is Salem Saberhagen?

a) The talking cat on *Sabrina, the Teenage Witch*
b) The family dog on *Married…with Children*
c) *The Flintstones* family pet

ANSWERS: 1.A 2.B 3.B 4.B 5.A

Thoughts of the Throne

The first Charmin commercial was filmed, appropriately, in Flushing, New York.

The Fantastic Four

1. Joe, Murr, Sal and Q make up the foursome of real-life friends who star on what hidden camera show?

a) *Impractical Jokers*
b) *Crank Yankers*
c) *Scare Tactics*

2. Of *Sex and the City's* four leading ladies, three were in their 30s and one in her 40s. Who was the elder member of the group?

a) Charlotte York (Kristin Davis)
b) Miranda Hobbes (Cynthia Nixon)
c) Samantha Jones (Kim Cattrall)

3. On what show do Vince, E, Turtle and Johnny Drama live the Hollywood lifestyle after growing up together in Queens, New York?

a) *Eastbound & Down*
b) *Entourage*
c) *Flight of the Conchords*

4. The voices of *South Park's* Stan, Cartman, Kyle and Kenny are all provided by the show's creators. Who are they?

a) Trey Parker and Matt Stone
b) Joel and Ethan Coen
c) Sean Parker and Peter Theil

5. By what name were Howling Mad Murdock, B.A. Baracus, Hannibal Smith and Templeton Peck better known?

a) *The A-Team*
b) *The Mod Squad*
c) *Hogan's Heroes*

ANSWERS: 1.A 2.C 3.B 4.A 5.A

May you fall asleep under a camel with post-nasal drip.

-Carnac the Magnificent,
The Tonight Show Starring Johnny Carson

Family Matters

1. George Wendt, who played Norm on *Cheers*, is the uncle of what *Saturday Night Live* cast member?

a) Bill Hader
b) Jason Sudeikis
c) Fred Armisen

2. Brothers Fred and Ben Savage came to fame as child actors on what respective TV shows?

a) *Saved By the Bell* and *Home Improvement*
b) *Blossom* and *Dawson's Creek*
c) *The Wonder Years* and *Boy Meets World*

3. Real-life couple Jerry Stiller and Anne Meara were married on the final season of what sitcom?

a) *King of Queens*
b) *Seinfeld*
c) *Friends*

In 1950, the town of Hot Springs, New Mexico, renamed itself *Truth or Consequences* after the popular game show. Host Ralph Edwards announced that he would air the program from the first town that renamed itself after the show. He kept his word.

4. What is the relationship between famous TV figures Garry Marshall and Penny Marshall?

a) Husband and wife
b) Brother and sister
c) Father and step-daughter

5. Allison Williams, daughter of TV news personality Brian Williams, starred in the title role of what musical that aired live on NBC in late 2014?

a) *Robin Hood*
b) *Peter Pan*
c) *Cinderella*

ANSWERS: 1.B (Wendt is his mother's brother.) 2.C 3.A 4.B 5.B

If you were singing like this two thousand years ago, people would have stoned you.

-Simon Cowell, *American Idol*

Before They Were Famous

1. Pat Sajak and David Letterman held the same TV position before they made it big hosting their own shows. What was it?

a) News anchor
b) Sportscaster
c) Weatherman

2. Before she was C.J. Parker on *Baywatch*, Pamela Anderson's first recurring TV role came as "Lisa" on what 1990s sitcom?

a) *Family Matters*
b) *Coach*
c) *Home Improvement*

3. The first TV role for what current movie star came in 1992 as a re-enactor on an episode of *Unsolved Mysteries*?

a) Leonardo DiCaprio
b) Matthew McConaughey
c) Matt Damon

4. What comic actor appeared on TV in the late 1980s as Theo Huxtable's friend, Smitty, in *The Cosby Show*?

a) Owen Wilson
b) Adam Sandler
c) Ben Stiller

5. *Wheel of Fortune's* Vanna White and *Breaking Bad's* Aaron Paul were both contestants on what game show before either was in the public eye?

a) *Hollywood Squares*
b) *Family Feud*
c) *The Price Is Right*

ANSWERS: 1.C 2.C (She was the original "Tool Time" girl.) 3.B 4.B 5.C

We all have to live with our disappointments...
I have to sleep with mine.

-Al Bundy, *Married...with Children*

Killer Trivia

1. Who shot J.R.?

a) Cliff Barnes
b) Sue Ellen Ewing
c) Kristin Shepard

2. T.R. Knight portrayed George O'Malley, a character who shockingly died on what show?

a) *Lost*
b) *Grey's Anatomy*
c) *24*

3. What leading man in *Game of Thrones* was killed off at the conclusion of the first season?

a) Jon Snow
b) Ned Stark
c) Varys

Before Ed Sullivan became well known as the host of his own TV entertainment show on Sunday nights, he was a theater critic. In his very first review, he opined that playwright August Strindberg should consider rewriting the second act of his play *The Father*. The only problem-Strindberg had been dead for almost a decade.

4. On *Seinfeld*, George's fiancee Susan died in a very unusual manner. What happened?

a) She was poisoned from the glue that she licked on the envelopes to their wedding invitations.
b) She fell off a cliff after Kramer accidentally hit her with a loaf of bread.
c) She crashed her car into an ice cream truck minutes after an argument with George about which Ben & Jerry's flavor was the best.

5. Among all the deaths in *The Sopranos*, arguably none was more surprising than the fiancee of Tony Soprano's protege, Christopher Moltisanti. What was her name?

a) Patsy Parisi
b) Adriana La Cerva
c) Jennifer Melfi

ANSWERS: 1.C 2.B 3.B (played by Sean Bean) 4.A 5.B

Thoughts of the Throne

The first toilet flush heard on television came from Archie Bunker's upstairs bathroom on *All in the Family*.

Criminal Minds

1. In *Dexter*, Michael C. Hall stars as the title character, a blood spatter pattern analyst who leads a secret life as a serial killer. What is Dexter's last name?

a) Andrews
b) Oliver
c) Morgan

2. The casting of HBO's *The Wire* included several recurring appearances by real-life figures in what U.S. city where the show is set?

a) Detroit
b) Memphis
c) Baltimore

3. In *Ray Donovan*, the title character, played by Liev Schreiber, works as a professional "fixer", arranging for bribes and payoffs, in what powerful law firm?

a) Goldman & Drexler
b) Lockhart Gardner
c) Wolfram, Hart and Donowitz

4. The creator of HBO's *True Detective* was previously a writer on a fellow crime drama, *The Killing*. Who is he?

a) Simon Blackwell
b) Nic Pizzolatto
c) Eric Overmyer

5. "This is a true story. The events depicted took place in Minnesota in 2006. At the request of the survivors, the names have been changed. Out of respect for the dead, the rest has been told exactly as it occurred." What show is the text from?

a) *The Following*
b) *Fargo*
c) *Hannibal*

ANSWERS: 1.C 2.C 3.A 4.B 5.B

Now I have to go back and arrest my girlfriend for conspiracy and attempted murder. She'll probably break up with me.

-Lt. Randall Disher, *Monk*

That's All, Folks!

1. "Goodbye, Farewell and Amen" was the title of the episode for this sitcom's last show, the most watched TV series finale ever.

a) *Cheers*
b) *Magnum, P.I.*
c) *M*A*S*H*

2. Who were the last two guests to appear on *The Tonight Show with Johnny Carson* in May of 1992?

a) David Brenner and Bob Hope
b) Robin Williams and Bette Midler
c) Joan Rivers and Barry Manilow

3. In a major twist, the famous ending of what series reveals that its eight seasons had all simply been a dream?

a) *Lost*
b) *Newhart*
c) *Everybody Loves Raymond*

4. The oft-criticized *Seinfeld* finale ends with Jerry doing stand-up to a hostile crowd in what setting?

a) Prison
b) Alcoholics Anonymous meeting
c) Nursing home

5. Before the screen turns black, “I went ahead and ordered some for the table” are the last words ever said in what show?

a) *24*
b) *Dallas*
c) *The Sopranos*

ANSWERS: 1.C 2.B 3.B 4.A 5.C

I'm not really a cab driver. I'm just waiting for something better to come along. You know, like death.

-Alex Reiger, *Taxi*

Signing Off

I will never understand why they cook on TV. I can't smell it, can't eat it, can't taste it. At the end of the show they hold it up to the camera: "Well, here it is. You can't have any. Goodbye."

–Jerry Seinfeld

•

Ever watch the TV show *Cops*? It's actually a pretty educational show. The most important thing I learned from watching is the one way to avoid being arrested is to wear a shirt.

–Dennis Regan

•

Why would anyone play *Jeopardy!* now? Hard questions for $500. On the other shows you can say how many people are in the Jackson Five for a million.

–Chris Rock

•

I don't know what's wrong with my television set. I was getting C-SPAN and the Home Shopping Network on the same station. I actually bought a congressman.

–Bruce Baum

In Russia we only had two TV channels. Channel One was propaganda. Channel Two consisted of a KGB officer telling you, "Turn back at once to Channel One!"

–Yakov Smirnoff

•

I don't care what sport he's watching on TV, my husband says, "C'mon, there's only two minutes left in the game." Those are the longest two minutes in the universe. Where do you get this clock? I'd like one in my bedroom.

–Cory Kahaney

•

The worst thing about television is that everybody you see on television is doing something better than what you're doing. You never see anybody on TV just sliding off the front of the sofa, with potato chip crumbs all over their shirt.

–Jerry Seinfeld

Thoughts of the Throne

In Russia the big TV show is Who Wants to Win a Roll of Toilet Paper? *No one's won a whole roll yet.*

-Jay Leno

I watch the Discovery Channel, and you know what I've discovered? I need a girlfriend. The more Discovery Channel you watch, the less chance you ever have of meeting a woman, because it fills your head full of odd facts that can come out at any moment. "Hello. Did you know Hitler was ticklish? That the sea otter has had four nipples? Don't run away!"

–Dave Attell

•

One night I walked home very late and fell asleep in somebody's satellite dish. My dreams were showing up on TVs all over the world.

–Steven Wright

•

Your cable television is experiencing difficulties. Please do not panic. Resist the temptation to read or talk to loved ones. Do not attempt sexual relations, as years of TV radiation have left your genitals withered and useless.

–Homer Simpson